D0944120

Edition Eulenburg

A son ami Pablo de Sarasate

SYMPHONIE ESPAGNOLE

D minor
for
Violin with Orchestra

by

EDOUARD LALO

Op. 21

First performed 7th February, 1875
at Paris, Concerts populaires
with Sarasate as soloist

Ernst Eulenburg, Ltd. London, W.1.
Edition Eulenburg, G.m.b.H., Zurich
Edition Eulenburg, K.-G. Stuttgart
Eulenburg Miniature Scores, New York

Pag.

I.   Allegro non troppo 1

II.   Scherzando. Allegro molto 41

III. Intermezzo Allegretto non troppo . . . 71

IV.   Andante 98

V.   RONDO. Allegro III

Symphonie espagnole

I

Edouard Lalo, Op. 21
1823 - 1892

Ausgabe mit Pianofortebegleitung neu bearbeitet von Rob. Reitz
No. 728   E. E. 3818   Ernst Eulenburg Ltd., London - Zurich

E.E. 3818

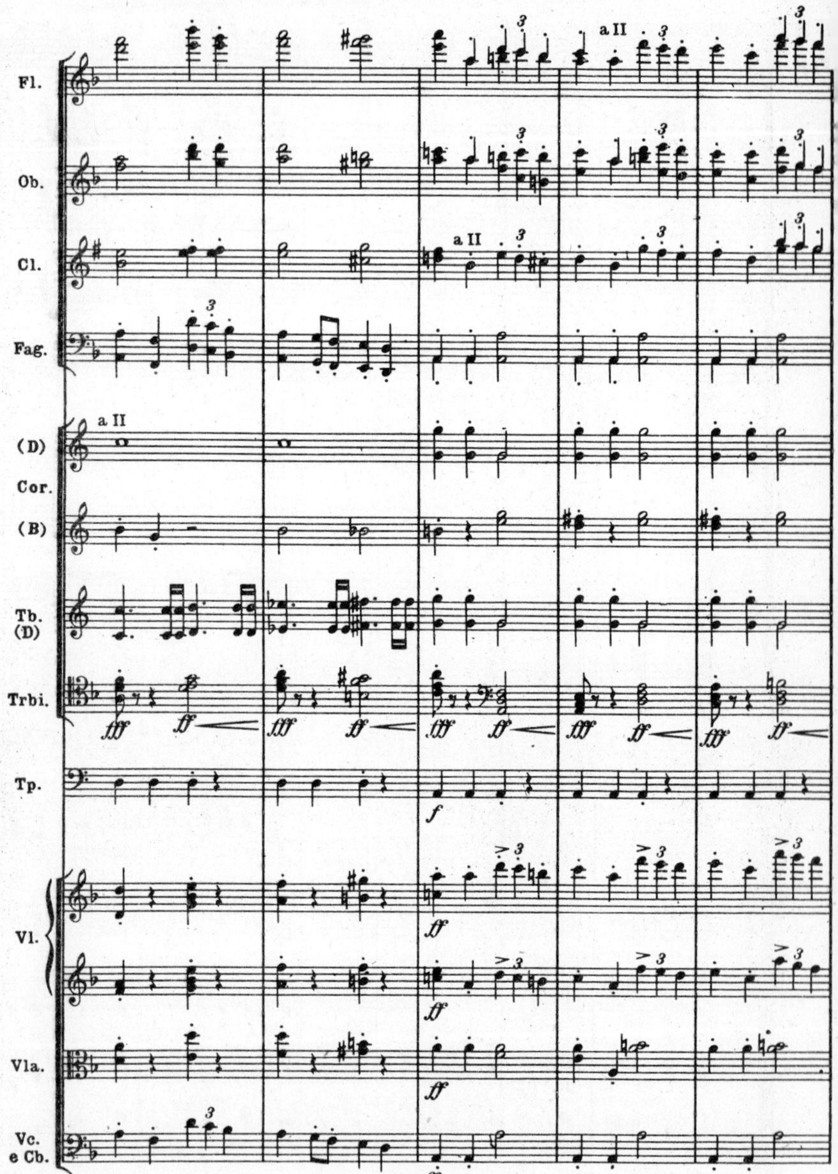
Fl.
Ob.
Cl.
Fag.
a II
(D)
Cor.
(B)
Tb.
(D)
Trbi.
fff
ff
Tp.
f
Vl.
Vla.
Vc.
e Cb.

B

16

E. E. 3818

E. E. 3818

E. E. 3818

F

E.E. 3818

E. E. 3818

E. E. 3818

30

E.E. 3818

32

E. E. 3818

35

E. E. 3818

E. E. 3818

38

E. E. 3818

II
Scherzando

E. E. 3818

43

E. E. 3818

45

E. E. 3818

46

48

E. E. 3818

50

E. E. 3818

58

Tempo I

64

E. E. 3818

III
Intermezzo

Allegretto non troppo (♩ = 66)

E. E. 3818

74

E. E. 3818

75

E.E. 3818

80

E. E. 3818

84

E.E. 3818

Fl. picc.
Fl.
Ob.
Cl.
Fag.
(A)
Cor.
(E)
Tb.
(D)
Trbi.
Tp.
Vl. pr.
Vl.
Vla.
Vc.
e Cb.
sec.
f
ff
arco
8

90

E. E. 3818

E.E.3818

92

*) In der Viol.-Solostimme:

E.E. 3818

E. E. 3818

IV

100

E.E.3818

E. E. 3818

102

C

E. E. 3818

E. E. 3818

106

E.E.3818

E. E. 3818

V
Rondo

Allegro ($\bullet$. = 108)

Fl.picc.
Fl.
Ob.
Cl.
Fag.
(D)
Cor.
(F)
Tb.
(D)
Trbi.
Tp.
Tamb.
Trgl.
Ap.
Vl.
Vla.
Vc.
Cb.
dim.
f
mf
p
pizz.
II
8

115

E. E. 3818

120

E. E. 3818

122

E. E. 3818

E. E. 3818

126

E. E. 3818

127

E.E.3818

E. E. 3818

132

E. E. 3818

G Poco più lento (♩ = 96)

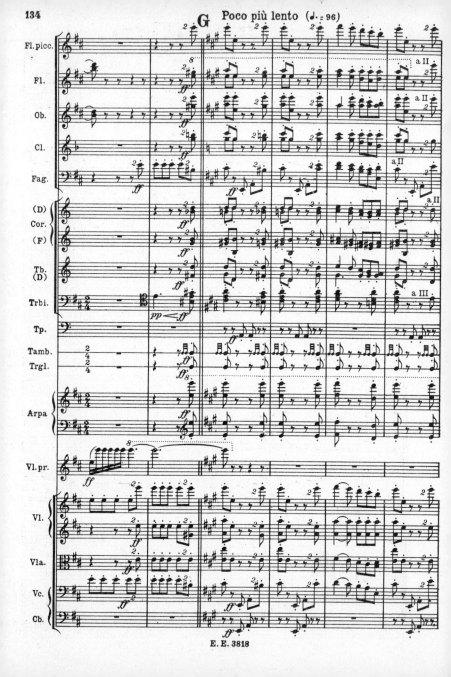

136

138

Tempo I *(Allegro)* (♩. = 104.)

145

E. E. 3818

senza rallentare

E. E. 3818

154

158

SYMPHONIES

No.
401. **Mozart,** C (Jupiter) [551] ....
402. **Beethoven,** No. 5, C m ....
403. **Schubert,** B m (unfinished) ....
404. **Mozart,** G m [550] ....
405. **Beethoven,** No. 3, E♭ (Eroica) ....
406. **Mendelssohn,** Nr. 3, A m ....
407. **Beethoven,** No. 6, F (Pastorale) .....
408. **Schumann,** No. 3, E♭ ....
409. **Haydn,** No. 104, D (London) ....
410. **Schubert,** No. 7, C ....
411. **Beethoven,** No. 9, D m ....
412. **Beethoven,** No. 7, A ....
413. **Schumann,** No. 4, D m ....
414. **Beethoven,** No. 4, B♭ ....
415. **Mozart,** E♭ [543] ....
416. **Beethoven,** No. 8, F♭ ....
417. **Schumann,** No. 1, B♭ ....
418. **Beethoven,** No. 1, C ....
419. **Beethoven,** No. 2, D ....
420. **Mendelssohn,** Nr. 4, A ....
421. **Schumann,** No. 2, C ....
422. **Berlioz,** Phant. Symph ....
423. **Berlioz,** Harold i. Ital............
424. **Berlioz,** Romeo and Juliet ....
425. **Brahms,** No. 1, C m..............
426. **Brahms,** No. 2, D ....
427. **Brahms,** No. 3, F................
428. **Brahms,** No. 4, E m ....
429. **Tschaikowsky,** No. 5, E m ....
430. **Tschaikowsky,** No. 4, F m ....
431. **Haydn,** No. 99, [3], E♭....... .....
432. **Haydn,** No. 85, [15], B♭ (La Reine)....
433. **Dvořák,** No. 5, E m (New World)....
434. **Haydn,** No. 100, G (Mil.)..........
435. **Haydn,** No. 94, G (Surprise)........
436. **Haydn,** No. 92, G (Oxf.) ....
437. **Mozart,** D [385] (Haffner)..........
438. **Haydn,** No. 102, B♭ ....
439. **Haydn,** No. 101, D (Cloches) ....
440. **Strauss,** Don Juan ....
441. **Strauss,** Macbeth ....
442. **Strauss,** Death and Transfig. ....
443. **Strauss,** Till Eulenspiegel ....
444. **Strauss,** Zarathustra ....
445. **Strauss,** Don Quixote ....
446. **Mozart,** D [504] ....
447. **Liszt,** Montagne.................
448. **Liszt,** Tasso ....
449. **Liszt,** Préludes................
450. **Liszt,** Orpheus ....
451. **Liszt,** Prometheus...............
452. **Liszt,** Mazeppa ....
453. **Liszt,** Festival Sounds ....
454. **Liszt,** Heroic Elegy..............
455. **Liszt,** Hungaria ....
456. **Liszt,** Hamlet.................
457. **Liszt,** Battle of Huns ....
458. **Liszt,** Ideals ....
459. **Bruckner,** No. 1, C m ....
460. **Bruckner,** No. 2, C m ....
461. **Bruckner,** No. 3, D m ....
462. **Bruckner,** No. 4, E♭ (romantic).....
463. **Bruckner,** No. 5, B♭ ....

No.
464. **Bruckner,** No. 6, A ....
465. **Bruckner,** No. 7, E ....
466. **Bruckner,** No. 8, C m ....
467. **Bruckner,** No. 9, D m ....
468. **Haydn,** No. 93, D ....
469. **Haydn,** No. 103, E♭ (Drum Roll).....
470. **Volkmann,** No. 1, D m ....
471. **Smetana,** Vysehrad ....
472. **Smetana,** Moldau ....
473. **Smetana,** Sarka ....
474. **Smetana,** Bohemia's Woods and Fields ....
475. **Smetana,** Tábor ....
476. **Smetana,** Blanik.................
477. **Liszt,** Faust-Symph.............
478. **Strauss,** From Italy..............
479. **Tschaikowsky,** No. 6, B m (Pathétique) ....
480. **Haydn,** No. 95, C m.............
481. **Haydn,** No. 96, D ....
482. **Franck,** D m ....
483. **Haydn,** No. 97, C ....
484. **Haydn,** No. 86, D ....
485. **Haydn,** No. 98, B♭ ....
486. **Haydn,** No. 45, F♯m (Farewell).....
487. **Haydn,** No. 88, G ....
488. **Haydn,** No. 82, C (L'ours)..........
489. **Rimsky-Korsakow, Antar** (No. 2).
490. **Borodin,** No. 1, E♭.............
491. **Borodin,** No. 2, B m ....
492. **Mahler,** No. 7 ....
493. **Rimsky-Korsakow,** Scheherazade...
494. **Glasunow,** No. 4, E♭............
495. **Glasunow,** No. 8, E♭............
496. **Skrjabin,** Divin Poème ....
497. **Skrjabin,** Le Poème de l'Extase.....
498. **Strauss,** Hero's Life.............
499. **Strauss,** Alpine Symph...........
500. **Tschaikowsky,** Manfred...........
501. **Borodin,** No. 3, A m (unfinished).....
502. **Mozart,** C [425]................
503. **Skrjabin,** No. 2, C m ....
504. **Schubert,** No. 1, D.............
505. **Schubert,** No. 2, B♭............
506. **Schubert,** No. 3, D.............
507. **Schubert,** No. 4, C m (Tragic) ......
508. **Schubert,** No. 5, B♭............
509. **Schubert,** No. 6, C ....
510. **Strauss,** Domestica ....
511. **Haydn,** No. 73, D (Chasse) ....
512. **Haydn,** No. 31, D (Hornsignal)......
513. **Haydn,** No. 7, C (Le Midi) ....
514. **Franck,** Chasseur maudit ....
515. **Haydn,** No. 8, G (Le Soir)..........
516. **Franck,** Les Eolides ....
517. **Haydn,** No. 48, C (Maria Theresia)...
518. **Haydn,** No. 55, E♭ (Schoolmaster) ...
521. **J.Chr.Bach,** D ....
522. **J.Chr.Bach,** E♭ ....
523. **Franck,** Rédemption ....
524. **Zador,** Dance Symph ....
525. **Dvořák,** No. 4, G ....
526. **Dvorak,** No. 2. D m ....

OVERTURES

No.
601. **Beethoven,** Leonore No. 3 ....
602. **Weber,** Freischütz.................
603. **Mozart,** Figaro ....
604. **Beethoven,** Egmont ....
605. **Weber,** Ruler of the Spirits.........
606. **Mendelssohn,** Melusine............
607. **Weber,** Oberon ....
608. **Mozart,** Don Giovanni.............
609. **Weber,** Preziosa ....
610. **Beethoven,** Fidelio ....
611. **Mendelssohn,** Ruy Blas ....
612. **Weber,** Jubelee ....
613. **Mendelssohn,** Mid. Night's Dream...
614. **Mozart,** Magic Flute ....
615. **Nicolai,** Merry Wives ....
616. **Rossini,** William Tell ....
617. **Berlioz,** Waverley.................
618. **Berlioz,** Judges of Secret Court.....
619. **Berlioz,** King Lear ....
620. **Berlioz,** Roman Carneval ....
621. **Berlioz,** Corsaire ....
622. **Berlioz,** Benv. Cellini.............
623. **Berlioz,** Beat and Bened. ....
624. **Tschaikowsky,** 1812 ....
625. **Beethoven,** Prometheus............
626. **Beethoven,** Coriolanus ....
627. **Beethoven,** Consecration ....
628. **Beethoven,** Leonore No.1 ....
629. **Beethoven,** Leonore, No. 2 ....
630. **Beethoven,** Ruins of Athens........
631. **Beethoven,** King Stephan ....
632. **Beethoven,** Name Day ....
633. **Marschner,** Hans Heiling ....
634. **Maillart,** Dragons de Villars ....
635. **Weber,** Euryanthe ....
636. **Schubert,** Rosamunde ....
637. **Mendelssohn,** Hebrides ....
638. **Glinka,** Life for the Tsar ....
639. **Glinka,** Ruslan and Ludmila ....
640. **Cherubini,** Abencerages ....
641. **Cherubini,** Medea..................
642. **Cherubini,** Anacreon ....
643. **Cherubini,** Water Carrier...........
644. **Cornelius,** Barber of Baghdad.......
645. **Cornelius,** Cid.....................
646. **Schumann,** Manfred ....
647. **Schumann,** Genoveva ....
649. **Wagner,** Tristan u. Isolde ....
650. **Boieldieu,** White Lady ....
651. **Auber,** Bronze Horse ....
652. **Wagner,** Lohengrin: (Act I and III) ..
653. **Mendelssohn,** Calm Sea and Pros-
    perous Voyage ....
654. **Rossini,** Semiramis.................
655. **Rossini,** Tancredi..................
656. **Brahms,** Acad. Fest. Ov. ....
657. **Brahms,** Tragic Ov...........
658. **Auber,** Black Domino ....
659. **Auber,** Fra Diavolo ....
660 **Mozart,** Tito....................

No.
661. **Mozart,** Idomeneo ....
662. **Mozart,** Cosi fan tutte ....
663. **Mozart,** Abduction ....
664. **Smetana,** Bartered Bride ....
665. **Wagner,** Mastersingers......   ...
666. **Wagner,** Parsifal..................
667. **Wagner,** Rienzi ....
668. **Wagner,** Dutchman ....
669. **Wagner,** Tannhäuser ....
670. **Reger,** Comedy Ov. ....
671. **Wagner,** Faust Overt...............
673. **Volkmann,** Richard III. ....
674. **Volkmann,** Fest-Ouv. ....
675. **Tschaikowsky,** Romeo ....
676. **Gluck,** Iphigenie in Aulide ....
677. **Smetana,** Libussa.................
678. **Suppe,** Poet and Peasant ....
679. **Flotow,** Stradella ....
680. **Flotow,** Martha ....
681. **Bruckner,** G m (posth.) ....
682. **Mendelssohn,** Son and Stranger ....
683. **Mendelssohn,** Athalia ....
684. **Mendelssohn,** St. Paul.............
685. **Rossini,** Barber of Seville ....
686. **Rossini,** Thievish Magpie ....
687. **Pfitzner,** Palestrina, 3 Preludes .....
689. **Auber,** Dumb Girl of Portici........
690. **Dvořák,** Carnival ....
691. **Gluck,** Orpheus and Eurydice ....
692. **Rimsky-Korsakow,** La grande Paque
    Russe ....
693. **Lortzing,** Czar and Carpenter.......
694. **Kreutzer,** Das Nachtlager von Granada
695. **Mussorgsky,** Howantschina.........
696. **Weber,** Abu Hassan ....
697. **Weber,** Silvana ....
698. **Schubert,** Alfonso and Estrella .....
699. **Glasunow,** Festival Overt. ....
700. **Pfitzner,** Kathchen v. Heilbronn ....
1101. **Humperdinck,** Hänsel und Gretel...
1102. **Gluck,** Alceste ....
1103. **Strauss,** Bat ....
1104. **Lalo,** Le Roi d'Ys ....
1105. **Boieldieu,** Calif of Bagdad ....
1106. **Strauss,** Gipsy Baron ....
1107. **Verdi,** Forza del Destino ....
1108. **Verdi,** Vespri Siciliani.............
1109. **Cimarosa,** Secret Marriage.........
1110. **Rossini,** L'Italiana in Algeri........
1111. **Weber,** Peter Schmoll ....
1112. **Verdi,** Nabucco ....
1113. **Rossini,** Scala di Seta ....
1114. **Handel,** Rodelinde, Ballet Terpsicore
1115. **Tschaikowsky,** Hamlet ....
1116. **Debussy,** L'Apres'-midi d'un Faune .
1117. **Bantock,** The Frogs ....
1118. **Borodin,** Prince Igor ....
1119. **Mozart,** Impressario ....
1120. **Rossini,** Cenerentola ....